down with skool!

geoffrey Willans
and ronald searle

DOWN with SKOOL !

COLLINS
ARMADA LIONS

First published 1958 by Max Parrish & Co Ltd, London
First published in this Armada Lion edition 1973
by William Collins Sons & Co Ltd
14 St James's Place, London s w 1
Second Impression November 1973
Third Impression August 1974

© Geoffrey Willans and Ronald Searle 1958

Printed in Great Britain
by William Collins Sons & Co Ltd, Glasgow

CONTENTS

'O.K. COME IN'

'O.K. COME IN'

This is me e.g. nigel molesworth the curse of st custard's which is the skool i am at. It is uterly wet and weedy as i shall (i hope) make clear but of course that is the same with all skools.

e.g. they are nothing but kanes, lat. french, geog. hist. algy, geom, headmasters, skool dogs, skool sossages, my bro molesworth 2 and MASTERS everywhere.

The only good things about skool are the BOYS wizz who are noble brave fearless etc. although you hav various swots, bulies, cissies, milksops greedy guts and oiks with whom i am forced to mingle hem-hem.

In fact any skool is a bit of a shambles.
AS YOU WILL SEE.

ST CUSTARD'S:

this is st custard's our skool taken with my brownie but i made a bit of a bish and didn't get it all in. Anyway what i hav got in is probably quite enuff. That is the front door in front but you can't get in since the boys nailed it up you hav to go in somewhere behind which fortunately you can't see as it is most unsavoury. On the right is the fire escape which props up ths skool i think or the skool props it up i am not sure. It is good to get out by at night but if there is a fire it is quicker to use that drane pipe. It is still quicker to jump out but in my case they might take the blanket away chiz.°

° a chiz is a swiz or swindle as any fule kno.

BY THE CAMERA CLUB

A FEW UNHAPPY SNAPS FROM THE MOLESWORTH ALBUM

This is the east wing. St custard's hav a very interesting history if you are interested in hist which few boys are. It was built by a madman in 1836 and he made a few improvements before he was put in the bin e.g. the observatory to study worms, the fortifications to pot at game-keepers and that round thing which hav no use at all.

it is a wonder this one didn't bust the cammera it is peason, he is my grate frend which means we tuough each other up continually. Acktually he not bad tho we argue a lot saying am not am not am not am etc until we are called on to tuough up a few junior ticks.

This is gillibrand on the high diving board and we all sa go it go it. His pater is a general so he is not very brany you can't expect it n.b. he came down off the diving board after this he said he could do it any time pappy but did not feel like it toda chiz.

grabber who is head of the skool captane of everything and winer of
the mrs joyful prize for rafia work. His pater is very rich and hav a
super rolls enuff said. He is bigger than me so i must be careful.

Our skool dog thinking. He is planning to dash across the pitch and
pinch the cricket ball then bite the umpire in the leg which was super.
He is not bad but he scored a gole against us in one match.

fotherington-tomas. As you see he is skipping like a girlie he is uterly wet and a sissy. He reads chaterbox chiz and we suspeckt that he kepes dollies at home. Anyway his favourite charakter is little lord fauntleroy and when i sa he hav a face like a tomato he repli i forgive you molesworth for those uncouth words.

Gosh chiz this is molesworth 2 my bro he is uterly wet and a weed it panes me to think i am of the same blud. He is always eating and cheeks everybode. You kno when fotherington-tomas sa there are fairies at the bottom of his garden molesworth 2 sa there is a dirty old rubbish heap at the bottom of his then zoom away dive bombing sparows worms the skool dog and other poor dumb creatures. i diskard him.

Of course there are a grate number of other weeds and wets about the place but i hope this will give you some idea of st custards's which with all the other skools will explane why britain is what it is toda. There is nothing more to add about st custard's except that it smell of chalk latin books skool ink foopball boots and birdseed. Now read on.

HEAD BEAKS AT BAY

FROM BEAK TO TAIL

Headmasters are always very ferce and keep thousands of KANES chiz moan drone. With these they hound and persecute all boys who are super like sir galahad.

Headmasters are always very proud of their skools and think they are the best in the world in britain in space or at any rate better than the nearest one in the districk. They sa 'Ah ahem to tell the truth the boys are ahem ahem not er quite in fact just not the *type* we want.' A fine thing to sa with me around i must sa.

Second to swots headmasters like boys who are good at foopball and shoot goals then they can shout 'Pile in caruthers strate for goal' or other weedy things from the touchline.

Personally i am not good at foopball i just concentrate on hacking everbode. Headmaster yell at me he sa MARK YOUR MAN MOLESWORTH ONE what does he think i am the arsenal chiz. Acktually fotherington-tomas is worse than me he is goalie and spend his time skipping about he sa Hullo clouds hullo sky hullo sun etc when huge centre forward bearing down on him and SHOT whistles past his nose. When all the team sa you should hav stoped it fotherington-tomas he repli 'I simply don't care a row of buttons whether it was a goal or now nature alone is beattful.'

i do not think he will catch the selectors eye.

Every headmaster hav a study or sitting room with easy chair for boys to bend over in fact it is not so much the kaning we object to it is the smell of the cushions and all that fluff down there. Peason sa he once found 2/6 in the lining but i expect that was a woper he always tells them.

Otherwise there is a bookshelf to stare at when geting pi-jaw about why you are being kaned. We hav Comentary on bible (six vols) gone with the

Kane descend whack gosh oo gosh oo gosh.

ind, Ruff's guide to the turf and Rider of Murder
ange confiscated three years ago which head-
asters wife thort was wonderful.

Once i try wizard wheeze to put a curl inside
ousis then it will break the kane.

Tiptoe shuffle shuffle zoom down on fotherington-
omas and shave his curly locks. While he blub i stuff
e locks inside my trousis.

Go to study. Kane descend whack gosh oo gosh oo
osh and hares fly out like H-bomb xplosion. Kane
ndamaged so it is not such a wizard wheeze after all
ut Headmaster gets a piece of his wife's mind
making mess after maids hav been in). So
OYS triumphant agane WIZZ.

KANES I HAVE KNOWN
by N. MOLESWORTH

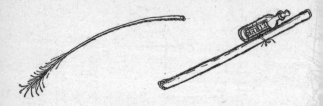

1. 'Old Faithful'. Whippy, no ferrule, 'palm-tree' ends. Can be thrown for dogs to fetch in the holidays.

2. The 'Nonpliant' or 'Rigid, with silencer attachment to drown victims cries.

3. 'Creaker' or split-seam. For use by 'hurt-me-more-than-it-hurts-you' kaners.

4. The first weapon he can lay hands on.

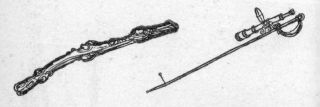

5. The 'Caber', Scotch-type for senior boys.

6. The hair-fine specialists kane for marksmen. Fitted with telescopic sights and range finder.

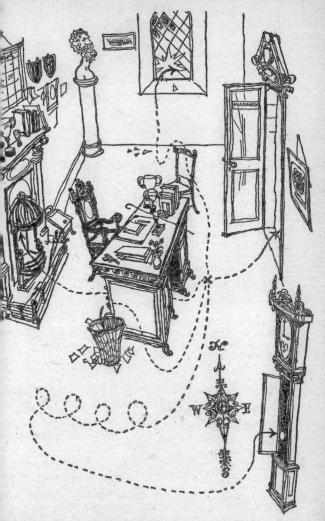

A headmaster's study with layout of the runways.

TWO SHORT SPEECHES FOR HEADMASTERS

TOGETHER WITH THE MOLESWORTH CRIB TO REEL THORTS

I *BEGINNING OF TERM*

Clang clang bell All sour-faced boys xsembl in skool hall.

HEADMASTER: (*with cheerful smile*) hullo basil hullo timothy hullo john did you hav a good hols?[1] How is your dear mother?[2]

(*to all more cheerful than ever*)

We hav twelve weeks ahead of us and i want you to cram[3] as much aktivity into them as you can in work and pla. This term we hav a new head of the skool grabber ma.[4] (*Claps noone join in*) You all kno the vertues we prize most loyalty and good influence.[5]

We expect grate things at foopball this term. grabber ma[6] is captain. We shall be a young side but do not forget david and goliath (*hearty larff*) a good little 'un is better than a good big 'un (*fits of larffter*) a terrier can worry a st bernard. (*he is going to die it is not good for him to larff so much*).[7]

CRIB TO REEL THORTS

(*N. moleswort knos all*)

1. So they are bac agane the litt beasts.

2. As if i care give me young m filips every time.

3. All they wil cram is my foo and tuck.

4. His father millionaire enu said.

5. Hem-hem ha to sa that sort o thing you kno.

6. Make him hea of anything for th usual amount.

7. Wot a han performance i'n giving.

8. He'd better o else.

9. who would ha thort it he seme so nice.

10. not too fathe fully i sincerely hope.

20

But perhaps grabber ma does not agree with that?[8]

I should like to introduce a new master who hav oined us in place of mr blenkinsop who left sudenly.[9] feel sure he will fill the place ocupied by his pre-lecessor.[10] . . .

etc etc until the bell ring for coco.

ANOTHER SPEECH

2 *PRIZE-GIVING AT THE SKOOL SPORTS*

HEADMASTER: (*tucking M.C.C. tie ver his clean dicky*) i should like to say now much my wife and i appreciate he grand turn-out of parents.[1]

i am sorry *all* the boys could not win a race but it is the sporting spirit which counts most.[2] i am happy to be able to tell you from matron that gillibrand 2 who fell on his nose in the sack race is not severely hurt.[3]

Each year it is my privilege to introduce the charming lade who give away the criket bats balls spoons cups etc.[4] 3 years ago it was the Duchess of Dabley, the following year Lady Hogtale, last year we were honoured by Royalty, and *this* year i am delited to sa a few words about another charming lade, as young as she is attractive—mrs grabber.[5]

CRIB TO THORTS

1. They hav eaten 29000 mackaroons and 5034 eclares. Wot do they think i am U.N.R.A.?

2. Only coshing from behind alowed in the obstacle race.

3. Pity.

4. Lucky i got 'em back from the pornbroker hemhem.

5. If that isn't good for a few thousand in the endowment fund i don't kno wot will.

6. for the ushual pament. They call me nero always fiddling.

7. How long can I go on with this?

8. Deep breath. Now for it.

21

(*Headmaster beams and claps loud cheers and yells.*)

It is all the grater pleasure as grabber ma hav won a
the races and is victor ludorum.[6] mrs. grabber herse
i think you will all agree showed where her sor
talent came from in the parents potato race.[7]

Therefore i welcome mrs grabber and thank he
for performing this task.[8]

(*A courtly bow, vast cheers, for she's a joly good felo,
etc. mrs grabber rises and begins speech: 'Cor strike a lite
never made a speech in me life. . . .'*)

MORE CHIZZES ABOUT
HEADMASTERS

It is a funy thing but headmasters are always ver
keen on conferences comittees etc when they discus
how to educate boys chiz tho it does not seme to mak
much diference we are all I G N O R A N T cheer
cheers cheers and do not kno the pluperfect of mone
i am glad to sa.

Another funy thing is that conferences always o
same day as oxford and cambridge, test match
wimbledon, rugby international or something of tha
sort. Coincidence? Anyway skool much more peace
ful masters slepe in the sunshine boys stretch beneth
tropic palms skool dog bites everbode when head
masters away so boo and snubs.

Headmasters all work v. hard. (See plan below)

A GAUL marching into Italy.

TIMETABLE OF DAY

0700.	Jump out of bed singing cheerful song chase the matron round the dorms pu sheets off masters beds rout out all boy to wash basins freeze freeze.
0710.	Chase out all boys who hav climbe back into bed.
0730.	Drive boys matron and masters int brekfast. eat wot the good lord ha provided as if truly thankful.
0736.	Greet wife with luving kiss.
0736.00001.	Stop greeting wife wipe moustache an eat more hadock.
0900.	Drive boys and masters into class. Loc them in. Take latin class qui quau quod stoke boiler peel potatoes mor latin quibus quibus quibus rush out t garden to pick sprouts mend punktur and answer leters.
1000.	Break. Milk buns boys for the kane
1015.	Drive in boys and masters agane la table clean silver feed hens teach 3 more latin. Romans v benevenuti Treble chance pool forum packed.
1300.	lunch stew and prunes. eat with relish
1330.	eat secret lunch smoked salmon ducl green peas strubres and cream.

1430.   Flay boys and masters from changing room to foopball field. coach boys remove corpses blow up foopball mend net. Demonstrate how to head ball. Fall stunned. Wake up in time to beat boys and masters back to change.

1600.   More latin. Benevenuti playing at home sla romans with spears and arows from ditches and ramparts. Wizz! About time romans got some new players put Caesar on the transfer list Aurelius inside-right and Remus into gole.

1800.   Tea bred and scrape.

1830.   Eat second tea meringues eclairs honey and sossages. Flog boys to bed. Chase matron round dorm. Lock masters in cells.

1930.   *BEER!*

2000.   Frugal super haunch of venison or rosted ox folowed by soup partridge wine jely and trifle. Push stale bred into masters cells. Prowl round dorm and kane raggers. Confiskate dormy feast and eat same.

2100.   Latin corections with left hand xxxxxxx xxxxxx do pools with the other xxooooo xxxxxx.

2200.   Snore.

A FEW HEADMASTERS

Mr Wesson thinks it's the ball-cock, Mrs Gordon thinks it's the shuttle pan. But *I* think it's you boys in fact I'm sure of it.

Come *on*, St. Custards.

That one, Postlethwaite, would have bowled Bradman.

Unless the culprit owns up the whole school will dig the vegetable garden.

This is *not* going to hurt me as much as it hurts you.

Procul procul o este profani.

He's holding up the whole side is Dick 2.

Your psycho-analyst may say one thing, Blatworthy, but I say another. And my treatment is *free*.

Mens Sana in Corpore Sano.

Facile Princeps.

Usque ad Nauseam.

Virtus in Arduis.

No reference is intended to any master alive or half-dead.

2

BOO TO SIR

or ARE MASTERS NESESSESSARY!

(Four theorems by permission of pythagoras now apearing at garison theatre aldershot.)

Masters are all shapes and sizes. Some are thin, some hav got an enormous pot on them some smoke cigs some smoke pipes poo gosh which ponk like anything and nearly ALL hav a *face like a squashed tomato.*
PROPOSITION: *All Masters are Weeds and Love the Kane.*
PROOF: The job of masters is suposed to be to teach boys lessons e.g. geog lat fr. div hist bot. arith algy and geom.

Aktually most of them prefer BEER and PUBS. They are always late for brekfast not like keen alert boys who goble force poridge cereal with grate gusto and look scorn on masters pale yelow faces when they see a skool sossage. Then is the time to ask Would you like some cream sir? or Gosh look at my egg sir its all runny. (Manners).

Masters do not care for brekfast and hav to be driven in to lessons by the headmaster chiz. They then sa get on with the next exercise and go to sleep snore snore. Q.E.D.

Then is the time to ask Would you like some cream sir? or Gosh look at my egg sir its all runny.

PROPOSITION: *Warning. Some Masters are Keen.*

PROOF: Keen masters are usually super weeds with specs. They rush into the classroom rubing their hands with joy at the thort of lessons and make a dash at the blakboard. They sit on pins needles rat traps hedghogs etc without jumping chiz they are so enthusiastick that all should learn.

Keen masters get on with the job at once they sa: 'Latin ex. forty-four a. Caesar where were we molesworth?' i do not repli as am removing toffe paper under desk. Master then sa: 'Where were we smith tomas matson one gillibrand two myers jonson jones' until he go through class. Of course noone kno as Caesar is uterly wet and a weed.

The thing about keen masters is that they are never discouraged. When you look at smith tomas matson one gillibrand two myers jonson and jones you could think they would put a gat or germ gun to their heads. But they do not chiz and all boys DRINK AT THE TREE OF KNOLWEDGE hem-hem i do not think. Q.E.D.

PROPOSITION: *Masters Are Swankpots.*

PROOF: Wise boys like me use FLATERY with masters from time to time e.g. When a master hav a new pair of shoes which is not often heaven knos molesworth 2 always sa About time too then run away.

My method is this i sa Oosir goshsir pleezesir what a super tie sir. The master repli Do you think so molesworth. You may stop your deten and pla foopball after all. WIZZ! SUPER!

Masters can often be tempted by this way to talk about wot they did in the war.

Masters hav always been brave in the war and it is a wonder they hav not all got the VC for capturing hitler holding the bridge etc. In fact if all the masters did wot they sa they did its a wonder we did not win the war in 1940.

Still it is not bad aktually as during a bit of parsing

or drawing a map of Spane you can just look up and
sa.

　'Did you hav a tomy gun during the war sir?'
　'Get on with your map mloesworth one.'
　'No but did you sir really?'
　'As a matter of fact i did molesworth.'
　'gosh sir did you shoot many germans sir.'
　'Get on with your map, boy.'
　'No sir but did you?'

They hav got to hav something in their lives besides Caesar
pythagoras and other weeds.

B

'Altho it hav nothing to do with the lesson i got g
thousand with one burst once . . . etc.'

The master will then go on for twenty minute
telling the class how he won the war etc just like pop
who was only in a weedy ack-ack brigade near
chiselhurst with a lot of soppy Ats and mum sa never
hit an aeroplane in his life.

Occasionally master's story is ruined by ass like
gillibrand whose pater is Major general sir gustave
godolfin gillibrand who ask: 'When you led your men
forward in the hale of fire sir was that not tacktically
unsound in view of the enfillade fire from numbers
two and three German patrols.'

Or perhaps molesworth 2 zoom by he is pretending
to be a meteor jet and he sa Able baker calling i bet a
million trillion pounds sir never saw a german at all
Able Baker out. He then go ah-ah-ah-ah-ah with
machine guns and sixteen chickens and skool dog bite
the dust he is a weed. Q.E.D.

PROPOSITION: *Masters Are Sloppy And Like Gurls.*
PROOF: Masters not only like BEER some hav
fotos of Gurls hem-hem like sabrina in their rooms. In
fact instead of thinking of NOTHING which i
wot most masters do they look more dopey than ever
they are in luv. That is all very well they hav got to
hav something in their lives besides Caesar pythagoras and other weeds but i ask you wot could any
GURL see in a master? Especially one like sabrina?
Q.E.D.

KNOW THE ENEMY
OR MASTERS AT A GLANCE

I cannot keep order.

The boys all look on me as a friend.

I am hoping to get a job in the colonial service somewhere.

I am keen on the latest developments in education.

I advise you strongly not to start ragging *me*.

You may think I'm soft but I'm hard, damned hard.

Mr Chips? No such character ever existed.

And when I asked him the supine stem of confiteor the fool didn't know.

I may not know much but I am
jolly good at football.

No. The spirit of tolerance,
you fool.

The crested grebes are
mating!

I am still hoping for a job in
the colonial service somewhere.

I was sent by the agency at the last minute before the term began.

A joke's a joke chaps but don't go too far.

I have been here thirty years. I have always said that and do not intend to change now.

Of course the fellow doesn't realize he's a typical schoolmaster.

3

A TOUR OF THE CAGES

or MASTERS ONE BY ONE

1. *ENGLISH MASTERS*

English masters hav long hair red ties and weeds like wordsworth throw them into exstatsies.

They teach english e.g. migod you didn't ort to write a sentence like that molesworth. For prep they always set an essay if they can think of one. In the good old days it was always something like:

What i did in the hols.

A country ramble.

A day at a railway station.

Now english masters are ADVANCED chiz and kno all about t.s. eliot cristopfer fry auden etc. etc and they read them so beatifully they make fortherington-tomas blub he is a sissy, and not worth a d. For essays english masters give us weedy things like —

A trip in a space ship.

my favourite machine gun.

what to do with masters.

you see wot i mean in the old days you knew where you were but now they are trying to read your inmost thorts heaven help them. Anyway you hav to write

40

them so as ushual boys are ground benethe palsied
heel of mummers. (auden.)

When english masters canot think of an essay they
set ten lines of Peotry.

PEOTRY

Peotry is sissy stuff that rhymes. Weedy people say la
and fie and swoon when they see a bunch of daffodils.
Aktually there is only one piece of peotry in the english
language.

The Brook
i come from haunts of coot and hern
i make a sudden sally
and-er-hem-er-hem-the fern
to bicker down a valley.

that is the lot tho the Charge of the light brigade
and the loss of the royal george are nearly peotry too.
Even advanced english masters set THE BROOK
they sa it is quaint dated gejeune etc but really they
are all in leag with parents who can all recite it. And
do if given half a chance.

Even gillibrand's pater General sir gustave godolfin
gillibrand sa THE BROOK is tip-top and com-
mend it to his men before going into batle insted of
RUM. Not a bad wheeze aktually but i would hav
an english master in front insted of a piper. In all
the bulets, wams, bonks and xplosions no english
master would escape his fate.

Sometimes we hav to recite which is girly in the

A ROMAN marching into Gaul.

extreme and there is no chance to read famous
CRIB which you copied out in prep.
  when i recite it is something like this:

> Tomow and tomow and tomow
> Um ah um ah
> Tomow and tomow and tomow
> Um – ah creeps creeps in the last syll—
> No!
> Tomowandtomowandtomow
>   Creeps in this um um
>   Out!
>   OUT!
>   brief candle
>   Yes i kno sir half a mo sir
>   Yes
>   fie
>   O fie!
>   Um um tis an unweeded syllable an un—
>   No!
>   Tomowandtomowandtomow etc. . . .

  In other words quite frankly i just don't kno it.
  Also quite frankly
  I COULDN'T CARE LESS
  What use will *that* be to me in the new atomic age?
  Occasionally english masters chide me for this
point of view o molesworth one you must learn the
value of spiritual things until i spray them with 200
rounds from my backterial gun. i then plant the
british flag in the masters inkwell and declare a whole

o molesworth one you must learn the value of spiritual things.

holiday for the skool. boo to shakespeare.
So much for english masters.

LITERARY CORNER

A book for the hols. '*Rob Roy*' by *Charles Dickens*.
(*Grabber & Grabber* 6s.)

To judge from the first page which i hapned to see by
mistake this is something about a small boy who had
to climb chimneys. Acktually i would hav thort this
was quite super as you get black but this one seemed
to be rather sorry for himself. On page 5 there is a
pressed leaf and on page 77 some orange juice i spilt
while the book was acting as part of a fort. There
seemed to be something about some water babies or
something soppy but i don't really kno. i supose he
must hav climbed the chimney to rob roy but this is
only a guess.

2. *LATIN MASTERS*

Latin masters teach lat. which is different from eng.
geom algy fr and others becos it is first period after
break. (imagine puting lat. of all things after coco
and buns they ort to give us indigestion tablets which
FIZZ like mum hav with a hangover).

If you wake for long enuff you find that everything
in lat. hapned a long time ago. Latin masters therefore are always old and bent with age. You can hear
there footsteps a long way off thump thump shuffle
shuffle and can put all sweets bludgeons dagers,
coshes swords white mice cheese marbles or whatever
is hapning to engage your fancy back inside the desk.

Latin master finally make grate heave and toter
towards desk you would think it was mount everest.
Will he make it? Effort! He sits in the chair panting.

THE LESSON WILL COMENCE

Open hillard and botting turn to ex ia section 2 sentence 6.

If latin masters are slo starters, once they get a latin ex. they go like a jet rocket, in fact you would think they were runing in the darby like hard ridden only faster chiz.

They sa: 'The gauls – galli – subject – go on molesworth oppugnant – what does oppugnant mean – they are atacking fossas. Ditches. What did you say molesworth? Why on earth atack a ditch? Keep your mind on the sentence. The gauls are atacking the ditches. What? *I am quite unable to inform you molesworth for what purpose the Gauls wished to attack the ditches.* The latin is correct. That sufices.'

We proceed. sagittis. What's sagittis molesworth what case come along boy – sagitta sagitta sagittam first declension – *with* arows by with or from arows. What is that? molesworth for the last time your opinion that it is soppy to atack a ditch does not interest me. Or what you personally would do with an arow. nor do i kno where the bows are. Likewise the question of whether there was buckets of blud is immaterial. The gauls are atacking the ditches with arows – telisque – telisque, molesworth? . . .

Aktually the trick is to look dopey and then the latin master will do all the translation himself.

Latin prose is difrent. It is either about a weed called Cotta who is always beating the Belgians or about Romulus and Remus who are a couple of babies who founded the city of Rome chiz if only they had abstained there would be no lat and no one could sa hunc hanc hoc without being put in a sty with the skool pig and rightly too. Anyway latin masters would be out of a job if there was no latin so they keep it going.

All latin masters hav one joke.

Caesar adsum jam forte
or
caesar had some jam for tea.

n.b. a good roare of larffter will cut the leson by two minits six seconds or half a gender rhyme a ab absque coram de palam clam cum ex and e etc. wot rot eh i mean to say?

3. *FRENCH MASTERS*

Acording to ancient tradition no fr. master can keep order.

Whenever a french master apere in the doorway it is a signal for hale of ink pots rubers chalk and stink bombs poo gosh. The fr. master then loose his temper and sa:

mon diue canaille allez-hoop
or
my god they're at it agane.

n.b. if the fr master is english this amount of french is ushually beyond him. he sa:

turn it up 2B now now turn it up

(*tournez-le dessus maintenant*).

47

Acktually fr. masters seldom get a chance to sa anything either in eng. or fr. But sometimes the boys are exorsted with raging and glad of the rest so the fr. master speaks. He speaks then of M. Dubois who is uterly wet.

M. Dubois is tall, thin and weedy: he wears a bowler hat and is very respectable. Sometimes he is in the kitchen with Mme Dubois. Sometimes he is taking Rose Amelie Fifi and the little dog Tou Tou for a promenade in the gardens of the luxembourg. Sometimes he is in the garden and sometimes he is smoking a pipe in his study. In fact, the felow never does a stroke of work. In the afternoons he is back in the gardens of the Luxembourg pointing out plants and pigeons. He eats his dinner and goes to bed.

After M. Dubois comes Armand (lesson 5 du dela des).

Armand is a small boy who wear a striped shirt and a round sissy straw hat like a girly. One day Armand is eating his breakfast when his father sa Toda we go for our holidays au bord de la mer. Armand is thrilled he sa O Papa are there flowers by the seaside you can tell the sort he is. in any case there must hav been something wrong if they only told him he was going to dieppe in the morning.

Armand sa: 'May I take my buket and spade, Papa?'

'Yes,' said Papa, 'and your windmill.' (You see?)

'How shall we go to the station, Papa?'

'Yes I must hire a cab. On arriving at the station i shall pay the driver then i go to the guichet and buy

a signal for hale of ink pots rubers chalk and stink bombs.

our tickets. The porter will take our bagage to the compartment. In the compartment are two ladies, three dirty old men and a postman who is smoking a pipe.'

'Are there boats on the sea?' asks Armand so you can see that i think Papa is only taking him to dieppe in order to drown him.

There is also another character called papa rat. He is always eating cheese. He loves cheese. Mama rat loves cheese too. They hav ten little rats who love cheese. In fact, the whole business is unspeakably sordid.

Finally there is loptimisme and pessimisme which is pierre et jean who spend all day looking out of a window. Jean looks out of the careau bleu and sa helas il pleut the day est sombre. Pierre looks out of

49

the careau jaune and sa Houp la le solay brillent. Aktually they are both wrong as according to the pikture in my book there is a thick fog due to rubbing out rude saings with bungy.

All fr. masters hav a joke too if they manage to shout it loud enuff.

> Je suis i am a pot of jam
> tu es thou art a clot etc.

n.b. with a fr. master this roar of larffter can be xtended safely for as long as five minits or more. This can be xtended when peason hav his famous fit of hystericks when he put fruit salts in his mouth and fome as he fall writhing to the ground WIZZ. The whole form then help him to matron leaving the fr. master with fotherington-tomas papa rat M Dubois, Armand and PEACE reigns agane.

4. *MATHS MASTERS*

$$\frac{a \times b \ (c-d)}{d \times c \ (b-a)} \times \frac{pq+rs}{xg - nbg}$$

The above is what maths masters thrive on and explanes why they are so very stern strict and fearsome. noone in a class ever stirs as a maths master approche you can hear a pin drop and no wonder when you think of the above sum which is enuff to silence anebode.

The only way with a maths master is to hav a very worred xpression. Stare at the book intently with a deep frown as if furious that you cannot see the answer. at the same time scratch the head with the end of the pen. After 5 minits it is not safe to do nothing any longer. Brush away all the objects which hav fallen out of the hair and put up hand.

'Sir?' (*whisper*)

'Please sir?' (*louder*)

'Yes, molesworth?' sa maths master. (*Thinks: it is that uter worm agane chiz*)

'Sir i don't quite *see* this.'

nb it is esential to sa you don't quite '*see*' sum as this means you are only temporarily bafled by unruly equation and not that you don't kno the fanetest about any of it. [*Dialog continue:*]

'What do you not see molesworth?' sa maths master (*Thinks: a worthy dolt who is making an honest efort*)

SCENES IN THE LIFE OF

PYTHAGORAS

useful for conversations at luncheon with maths masters

'number six sir i can't make it out sir.'

'What can you not make out molesworth?'

'number six sir.'

'it is all very simple molesworth if you had been paing atention to what i was saing at the beginning of the lesson. Go back to your desk and *think*.'

This gets a boy nowhere but it shows he is KEEN which is important with maths masters.

Maths masters do not like neck of any kind and canot stand the casual approach.

HOW NOT TO APPROACH A MATHS MASTER

'Sir?'

'Sir Sir please?'

'Sir sir please sir?'

The Discovery of the Rhomboid.

'Sir sir please sir sir please?'

'Yes molesworth?'

'I simply haven't the fogiest about number six sir.'

'Indeed, molesworth?'

'It's just a jumble of letters sir i mean i kno i couldn't care less whether i get it right or not but what sort of an ass sir can hav written this book.'

(*Maths master give below of rage and tear across room with dividers. He hurl me three times round head and then out of the window.*)

Maths masters do not stop at arith and algy they include geom and to do this they hav a huge wooden compass with chalk in the end for the blakboard. The chalk make a friteful noise which set our deliceat nerves jangling my dear but this is better than doing the aktual geom itself.

Pythagoras puzzled by one of my theorems.

Pythagoras as a mater of fact is at the root of al geom. Insted of growing grapes figs dates and othe produce of greece Pythagoras aplied himself to triangles and learned some astounding things abou them which hav been inflicted on boys ever since.

Whenever he found a new thing about a triangl Pythagoras who had no shame jumped out of his bath and shouted 'Q.E.D.' through the streets of athens it a wonder they never locked him up.

To do geom you hav to make a lot of things equa to each other when you can see perfectly well tha they don't. This agane is due to Pythagoras and i formed much of his conversation at brekfast.

A few lazy parrallelograms basking on Mount Olympus
Pythagoras stalking them.

PYTHAGORAS (*helping himself to porridge*): Hmm. I
see the sum of the squares on AB and BC=the
square on AC.

WIFE: Dear, dear.

PYTHAGORAS: I'm not surprised, not surprised at
all. I've been saying that would come for years.

WIFE: Yes dear.

PYTHAGORAS: Now they'll hav to do something
about it. More tea please. There's another thing –
the day is coming when they're going to have to
face the fact that a strate line if infinitely pro-
tracted goes on for ever.

WIFE: Quite so.

PYTHAGORAS: Now take the angle a, for xsample.

A battle of giants. Pythagoras bends the angle A.

55

(His wife sudenly loses control and thro the porridge a.
him. Enter Euclid: another weed and the 2 bores go of,
together)

All this taken into consideration it is no wonder
that no cunning wheezes or super dodges can be
plaed on maths masters. You just hav to sufer so boc
to fractions long div short div decimals.

5. SINGING MASTERS

Singing masters are frequently fr. maths lat or geog
masters. This is becos when they first come up to the
headmaster and sa 'Any odd jobs going? Chop your
wood,' the head sa, 'Yes, you could take 2B in div.
geog. handiwork and carpenty but only if you pla
the organ and take singing as well.' Singing master
then touch his cap. 'Give you a bit of a jingle,' he sa
and take out a mouth organ at which headmaster
flee into the woods.

Singing master then sit on stool of skool piano as if
he could pla it with ring of worms and cads round
him. fotherington-tomas hand round books full of
minims crotchets etc which hav been made into
beetles by boys mischievous fingers dear dear wot wil
they be up to next. Master than sa Number 56 hearts
of oak class sing mightily and windows burst all over
the skool.

As singing masters stray into the job so to speak you
get all sorts and there is no real telling. i mean we had
one you kno the one with the super sports car

urum-urum-urum-uraaaaaa who used to sa O.K. hep cats snap into the boogie. which was super but the trouble with singing is headmasters hear it they can't help it. That master was soon in his sports car headed for town *urum-urum-urum-uraaaa* etc which was hard cheddar really.

On the other hand there are ones who sa lets hav a opera i mean to sa with our mob. Not that he didn't get a few weeds on his side and wot with fotherington-tomas as lieutenant pinkerton and molesworth 2 as tanhauser you couldn't hear yourself rag chiz.

Personaly it is not the noise i object to in music it is the words. i could not care less if i find the minstrel boy in the ranks of death the sooner the better he is uterly wet and unable to lift his fathers sword. On the other hand you can always put goldfish in the piano or something so if music be the food of luv pla on etc. fortissimo.

TABLE OF GRIPS AND TORTURES
FOR MASTERS

The plain blip for numskulls.

Side hair tweak exquisitely painful.

Single-hair extraction for
non-attenders.

The cork in the storm for
violent temperaments.

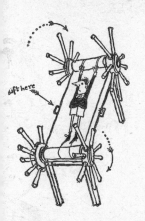

Portable rack for maths masters
(with thumbscrew attachment).

The headshave with ruler.

The Cumberland creep from behind with silver pencil.

The simple open furnace.

Aktually masters are not bad really and you hav got to hav them
They are absolutely like weeds becos when one goes another alway
aperes. (Som in fact are quite d. you might almost think they wer
human but on the whole i keep on with my batle cry DOWN
WITH THE USHERS. LET HONEST SKOOLBOYS
PREVAIL MASTERS UNFAIR TO MOLESWORTH.

60

4

LESSONS
AND HOW TO AVOID THEM

1. *BOTANY*

Hurra for the botany walk!

Now boys get into croc. Tinies in front seniors at the rear. Off for the woods and keep your eyes skinned. Ha-Ha – what do we see at once but a little robin! There is no need to burst into tears fotherington-tomas swete tho he be. Nor to buzz a brick at it, molesworth 2.

Pause at the zebra look left look right. Strate into the vicar's bicycle. That's all right we were none of us hurt and i canot believe that the vicar *really* said that grabber.

Ho for the woods agane!

Tread softly softly tippy toes. There is a bunny sprinting to its warren. And there a rook–one of the most fasscinating of the crow family. Keep that leaf for your pressings book, plunkett 2. You can see *what*, molesworth? A man-eating tiger? It hav a horible face with beedy eyes and weedy whiskers? i am sure you are mistaken. Ah, it was only the matron. Good afternoon, mato!

Now scater for specimens and when i blo the whistle scamper back to the fairy ring.

Peep!

Now

Wot hav we?

A dead bird, peason? i don't think that would find
its place in the nature museum it is so very dead. A
beetle a green spangle a brace of frogs. A worm,
molesworth? Ha-ha. I see a resemblance. A fern
frond, fotherington-tomas. I shall kepe it and wear it
on my hat.

To me all and let us be very silent. Wot do we
hear? Gillibrand bloing his nose? No, molesworth the
corncrake. CHIRUK – QUARK – HONK –
HONK – CHIRUK – QUARK. The corncrake is
a clever felow he is a ventriloquist and can thro his
voice. Did you sa he could thro it in the dustbin as
far as you are concerned, peason? That is not nice.
'Who were you out with Friday, baby?' Wot boy
said that? The corncrake, molesworth? I saw your
lips move i shall report you on return.

Fall into croc agane. Tinies in front. Back thro the
woods. Out into the road and cross by the zebra look
left look right. Cross! Ah, the vicar's bicycle agane.
What a coincidence! He *did* sa that word, grabber?
Which word? Oh.

Ho and away agane all!

This is the sort of chiz that miss pringle indulges
herself in with a botany walk. all boys are browned
off and could not care less if a bee place its long nose
into a flower and suck honey etc. or if anebode place
their long nose anywhere in the world in space. The
same goes for brite eyed creatures watching us from

FRAGRANT LEAVES FROM
MY BOTANY BOOK

A Glurk Trolling.

A Blue-nosed Chuck Brooding.

A Lesser Titwort Avoiding a Worm.

A Mongolian Thick Surprised (Rear View.)

their lairs. No wonder when they see our skool they all run away. i would do the same if i was a stoat.

HOW TO AVOID BOTANY

Suply yourself with a paket of cigs. When in woods ask permission to seek for a nest. Zoom away and climb a tree with peason or some other chump. Smoke a couple restfully. When ready return to fairy ring with three twigs and some straw then burst into tears a teeny ringtale ever so sweet hav been singing. Really botany make you sick – and if you smoke those cigs more so.

Boo to birds beats crows trees grass flowers also cristopfer robin and wind in the wilows. Charge at the tinies and mow them down.

2. *HISTORY*

History started badly and hav been geting steadily worse. It is like racing really when peason and i have a modest fluter thro the under gardener. All the favourites go down.

Harold beaten at Hastings.

Richard the Lion-Hart couldn't beat Saladin who was black as your hat.

Bruce victorious at Banockburn tho Scotish pack heavily outweighted.

Cavaliers beaten by the roundheads.

Finally beaten by the Yanks who thro all our tea into Boston harbour dressed like red indians that was the absolute end.

c

History began with a lot of barons who opresed everbode. Then they became respectable and agreed king john was going too far. Thou mayest hav the body they cried so he signed magna carta in xchange. When king john had got the body he didn't kno what to do with it of course. He ort to hav put a gun in its hand and make it appere like suicide chiz like in the detective stories.

Everything went on and people like Prince Rupert zoom about on their chargers at mach 1 or close to speed of sound. Meanwhile they discovered books and lots of people learned to read. This is nothing to boste about aktually as even molesworth 2 can read, but they thort it was wonderful and it all led to skools chiz chiz chiz.

It also led to KNOLEDGE.

A SERF: We are not hapy in our lot.

AN APRENTICE: Nor in our lot either.

This meant the Rise of the People and the People hav gone on rising ever since like yeast until you kno where they are now hapy and prosperus you ask them when the television programme is over.

And if you ask all those who hav gone before i am not sure whether they would agree that it is worth it. But it is too late now.

HOW TO AVOID HISTORY

Noone hav ever found a way of avoiding history it is upon us and around us all. The only thing when you look at the cuning vilaninous faces in our class you wonder if history may not soon be worse then ever.

UNTOLD HISTORY

How sir molesworth stormed the castle of sir sirloin de peason in Picardy. (The original is preserved in the fly leaf of his latin dictionary.)

How sir molesworth led the apprentices from the City stormed the skool and claped the headmaster in the Tower.

Sometimes you can get out of a hist. lesson by
EMING ILL. Pinch some flour from the kitchen
molesworth 2 hav not eaten it and rub well into
ace. After ten minits hold the brow and groan. The
ist. master stops in the middle of agincourt:

'Thou semest pale, molesworth 1. Is ort the mater?
Come, youth, impart wot ails thee.'

(*Note:* Hist. masters always talk like ivanhoe, blak
row etc.)

'No really sir i am quite alright.'

'Zounds it semeth thou hast the plague, good
kolar.'

'Nay, sirrah.'

(You talk like that too it is catching).

'But tis most remarkable i trow. Hi ye to matronnes
oom for a phial of phisick.'

'Nay nay sir no witches brew from yon crone shall
ver pass my lips.'

'But thy eye is bright with fever thou shakest with
palsy and would seme to hav the ague. Tis surely the
king's evil.'

'Does that put you off foopball. It is a chiz.'

Note: the real chiz about this method of avoiding
istory is that if the hist master go on long enuff you
begin to believe that death is really upon you. You
hav something wrong with your heart which hav
toped beating: your jaw is stuck open and you canot
close it also you are going blind. On the whole it is
peter to put up with the hist. lesson and draw beetles
on the blotch quietly or dab criket.

3. SCIENCE

Old fashioned skolars i.e. Tom Brown jan ridd 5th form at st dominicks etc. used to regard science as a joke. They called it stinks ha-ha which semed v. funy to them. They mixed lots of acids and powders in test tubes and the worse it smelt the more sucessful the lesson.

Progress is striking. Let us review some of the achievements of our science group. Here are some projects on which we are working. Forward the young elizabethans this is wot orange juice hav done for the world.

IN THE PLANNING STAGE

Long term. The peason-molesworth space ship to reach the moon in twenty years. By the time we are twenty we may hav worked out how to get back. Or will civilisation abandon us? Space ship is made out of a tin bath so we can keep clean when we get there.

Advanced stage: The plunket radio-controlled germ beamed to atack all masters.

The molesworth 2 thermometer with thermostatic control. Registers normal with matron and then pops up to 102.

The jet bowling attachments for criketers. Fits on arm and delivers ball at mach 8. Swerve off-break and googly atachment extra.

Quick-firing chalk gun for violent masters. Telescopic sights.

Electronick brane in difrent sizes. Does latin

70

sentences tots up sums Greek, French German speaking up to C. entrance standard. Answers everything and bafles masters.

All these are just wizard wheezes at the moment but all boys are plotting hard except molesworth 2 he is inventing the wheel as he feel in science nothing should be accepted he is utterly wet and couldn't hurt a flea.

Meanwhile new society of robot ant boys are pressing headmaster for better equipment. Why not a proton syncrotron to accelerate protons beyond 10 mil eh? We must make haste sloly sa headmaster.

All the same once we hav the syncrotron we shall all be a google eyed ant society. At the moment we hav the google eyes at any rate which is something especially peason. When we arive in our helicopters we shall take over the skool and feed all with cream. FREE THE SLAVES. WE LOOK TO THE DAY.

HOW TO AVOID SCIENCE

A good way in a science lesson is to wait until some old fashioned poison like sulphurick acid etc. turns up. As per ushual science master, who not forward-looking, sa: No boy is to touch the contents of the tube.

Make up tube which look the same and place alongside acid. Master begins lesson drone drone drone. Sudenly you spring to feet with grate cry: 'Sir Sir I can't stand it any longer!'

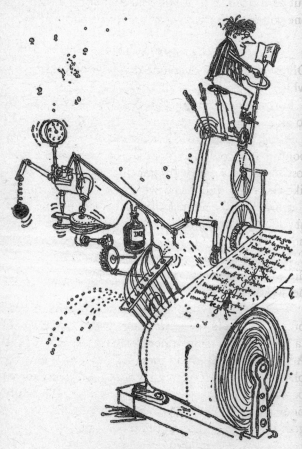

The Molesworth-Peason Lines Machine. Runs off
a hundred in one minit. (patnt pnding.)

Drink coloured water and collapse to be carried
out as if dead. n.b. if you make a mistake with this
one you are still carried out as if dead and you *are*.

4. *DIVINITY*

Div is super becos everyone do v. bludthirsty things
which are pleasing to all boys.

For instance Cain did his bro Abel which is enuff
to give me an idea occasionally about molesworth 2.

Abraham tried to do his small son isaac on the
bonfire. He would hav done him proper if he hadn't
lost his nerve i call it disgraceful with a little kiddy
like that who didn't kno wot his pa was up to.

David sa yar boo sucks to goliath and buzz a brick
at him. goliath fall stunned and wot david did then
no giant could ever forgive him i.e. he did him.

Some old girl whose name i canot remember also
did a chap with a tent peg a very nasty business when
he was asleep.

Then there was another nasty business about Saul
puting a chap in the front line in fact as mum would
sa the whole thing is rather like the news of the world.
Acktually i quite enjoy these tuough things but the
philistines who are absolutely super chaps always get
beaten in the end chiz. Anyway samson pull the whole
place down on top of everbode just when the story is
getting zciting so boo to the infant samuel.

HOW TO AVOID DIVINITY

You could try being let down by a rope into the class
dressed as an angel. You then sa to the master Lo who

You could try being let down into the class dressed as an angel.

re these cherubim and seraphim who are continually
rying. He repli Form 3B. You then sa Lo they are
not angles but angels with the xception of peason who
hav a face like a baboon. You must dismiss them
and the master oba.

On the other hand he may sa Lo molesworth do
200 lines. It is quite a good wheeze but probably
would not work.

5. GEOGRAPHY

END OF TERM GEOG PAPER WITH ANSWERS

*Students should write neatly marking name and form in the
right hand corner. Avoid the ushual blotches like atomic
xplosions. If you write a note to the next boy do not tear it off
your paper. Any boy will pass who slip examiner half a crown.*

(40 minits)

Q. What would you find at Hull?
A. Noone but a fool would ask this question. You
might find anything at Hull. It might be a razor
blade or an ear trumpet or a pair of bag-pipes it
just depends wot is lying around. In any case you
could find the same things in Ipswich. Be more
precise in future.
Q. What is a watershed?
A. A toolshed is where you keep tools a wood shed is
where you keep wood . . a watershed is where you
keep water. Don't waste my time.
Q. Are the Andes?
A. I ask you! Are the Andes? wot a question. Wot

does it mean clot? Do you mean *were* the Andes?
Of course they were. They didn't pop up
overnite you kno. Nor will they pop off agane
but i wish you would.

Q. in Africa?

A. i am waiting. the lunatick bin is second turning
on the right. they will be waiting for you. In
africa indeed! n.b. if the words 'in Africa' belong
to 'Are the Andes' i neither kno nor care.

Q. Where would you expect to find india ruber?

A. You never kno with a bungy it might be at the
bottom of the inkwell or it might hav been cut
into little bits for pellets. It might be all mixed
up with tooffe pen-knife stamps skoolboys diary
french coins etc in one of my pockets. If it is any
use to you fotherington-tomas hav a beatiful
pink bungy in that hole in his pencil box.

Q. From what tree do you get quinine?

A. You don't get quinine from a tree you ass. You
get it from matron on fridays. You wouldn't call
matron a tree. An old stick perhaps ha-ha-ha-ha
that is a good one. Next question.

Q. What are the positions occupied by the sun when
it is most remote from the equator and how many
are there in a year and on what dates? Does the
sun appear to remain stationary on reaching
these points? Is the sun vertical over the earth's
surface N. of the tropic of Cancer or South of the
tropic of Capricorn? What is an ecliptic?

A. A man who sufers from eclipsy.

Q. What is manioc?

A. Now you're asking. But who else whould hav
asked all these stupid q's eh?

HOW TO AVOID GEOGRAPHY

i should think that if you answer a paper like that you
might stand a good chance of never doing a geog-
raphy lesson agane at least not in that skool. it might
be better down a coal mine at least you get wages
which you don't at skool. You could try and see.

6. *GENERAL KNOWLEDGE*

General knowledge is all the stuff that is not covered
by latin geog algy geom fr. div. hist. etc. This is a lot
for a boy to stuff in his head especially if he could not
care less whether mountain goats are found in turkey.
The less i kno about mountain goats the better and
the same go for the height of the nelson column.

Lots of general knoledge these days is called
current events about the state of the world just to
cheer you up between latin and maths. gran you kno
gran who was a lade porter and made munitions
during the war hav been flying everywhere. She hav

been to friends in South Africa and New York and Singapore and now talking of zooming to rome for lunch in a comet. Pop sa you can't expect the world to be peaceful with her about and the whole Mess is due to her.

Aktually the Mess is due to the rusians who are roters. The points i wish to make about the world are contained in the molesworth newsletter.

(a) the rusians are roters.

(b) americans are swankpots.

(c) the french are slack.

(d) the germans are unspeakable.

(e) the rest are as bad if not worse than the above.

(f) the british are brave super and noble cheers cheers cheers.

The only way for Peace is for all of them to dive into the sea and end it all. This will leave the whole place to the mountain goats who inhabit turkey and they may make a beter job of it.

HOW TO AVOID GENERAL KNOWLEDGE

Ask the master whether he hav passed security check as integrated personality in global struggle against communism. Add Are you sir and hav you ever been a member of communist party then run like the wind.

A Gaul and a Roman passing each other in the Alps.

HOW TO SUCCEED WITH MASTERS

What is x+y+a—b, sir?   Gosh sir what a tie.

They're down there, sir.   But you told me to report to you
                                  and sa the whole of the Charge of
                                  the Light Brigade, sir.

Well kicked sir!

Look what we've got in here, sir.

You should hear what my pater
says about you, sir.

I suppose you can't *afford*
a car.

FLIGHT OF THE INK DART

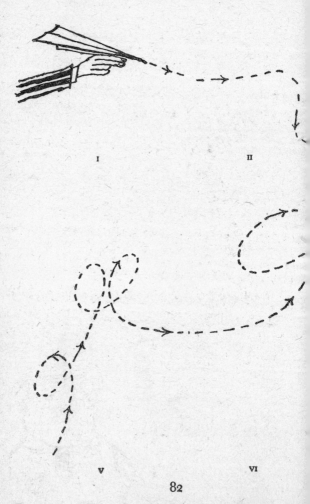

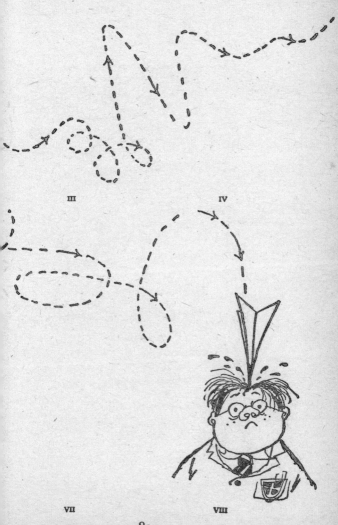

III IV

VII VIII

That's enuff of that for the moment. In the meantime *this*
should constitute a provocative action.

5

IN LOCO PARENTIS

*(For whom we are about to deceive
may the Lord make us truly thankful)*

Boys ushually hav 2 parents. These parents are very
like their dear children chiz chiz which shows that
you can look like peason or grabber or molesworth 2
and still get on in the world.

For some reason all these parents are anxious about
their dear little chicks and think they are the only
boy in the skool chiz wot a fate you'd have to make
up a class of masters. All mums think we are so
delicate we are going to pass out any moment its a
wonder they don't come down to the skool with a
bunch of lilies for the funeral.

Families often hav 2 grans on the strength borne
for critical duties and for making remarks i.e. wot a
curious smell skools hav in a v. loud voice.

You can tell the two grans apart becos one gran do
not aprove of your mater and your mater's mama
thinks your pater is selfish thriftless vague lazy
undependable untidy neglectful poor dilatory un-
reliable shiftless conceited helpless and an uter wet
who is not worthy of your mater's hand.

Grans are quite d. to boys however becos they
think poor little wretches blub blub none of it is their
fault with a pater and/or mater like that.

It seems strange that all the tuough boys around with faces like wild baboons started life as babes in prams chiz chiz chiz. i mean you kno wot weeds babes are they lie about and gurgle and all the lades sa icky pritty and other uterly wet things.

Being a baby is alright but soon all the boys who hav been wearing peticoats chiz chiz chiz begin to get bigger. they start zooming about like jet fighters climb drane pipes squirt water pisto s make aple pie beds set booby traps leave tools about the garden refuse to be polite to visiting aunts run on the flower beds make space rockets out of pop's golf bag and many other japes and pranks.

It is at this time that parents look thortfully at their dear chicks and sa

IT IS TIME WE SENT NIGEL TO SKOOL.

CHIZ!

Parents then search for a skool and dream of the day when the bath will not be full of plastic tugs speedboats queen marys etc. They look on the map until they find a place that is millions and trillions of miles away from home, and send for a prospectus.

The prospectus take a bit of time to arive owing to grate pressure of business on headmaster during term time (boat race, golf matches, University sports and international ruger). Finally headmaster enclose prospectus which was printed in 1914 and a bit dusty.

If headmasters were honest a prospectus would be

a book which sa how many kanes he hav, contane a warning about the skool dog and the amount of prunes and rice served during the term. Acktually it sa the skool is simply super just like claridges hotel chiz in fact when your pater see the fees he sa he could do three months in a suite at claridges more cheaply but this is just biterness. the noble boy must point out that if parents are to fob off dreadful offspring who climb drane pipes squirt water pistols etc no one is going to take him xcept for a fat price so boo and snubs to kruschev and the whole world.

AN IDEAL SETTING

st custards is splendidly situated in bracing downland country yet within easy reach of the town with main line railway station. A brook with clear sparkling water babbles by. It is a haunt for feathered folk who flock into the extensive grounds. The house is modern and nearby is the famous girls college. The air is tempered with sea breezes. An ideal setting for a seat of learning.

A CORNER OF THE PLAYING FIELDS

Games are a recognised part of the curriculum and matches are
played with neighbouring skools. The sporting spirit is fostered as
part of the skool tradition.

A PEEP INTO MATRON'S ROOM

Special attention is paid to health and all boys are under the super-
vision of a qualified matron who has at her disposal the full resources
of the sick room.

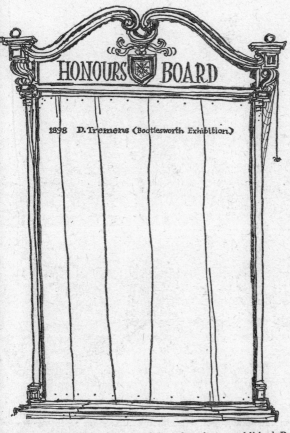

HONOURS BOARD

1898   D. Tremens (Bootlesworth Exhibition.)

The classical standards of st custards have long been established. Boys
are prepared for scholarship examinations. The school is recognised.

Boys are encouraged to develop their individual characters and
expand their personalities.

The Football Team

Played 8. Won o. Drawn o. Lost 8.

VISITING THE SKOOL

The day the parents come means much acktivity at the skool.

All rude drawings and propaganda down with the warmongers meeting at dalston friday are wiped off blakboards. Skool dog is muzled boys wash their necks and the bath is cleaned.

Next masters are let out of their cells in new suits mashers ties etc. and are forced by the headmaster to toe party line.

"Hav you been guilty of imperialist dogma in break by pinching a boys cup of coco?"

"I hav."

"Have you practised sabotage against the skool piano by cutting wires so that low C sounds plunk?"

"I hav."

"Do you admit this led to subversive singing of D'ye Ken John Plunk in his plunk so gay?"

"I do."

"Do you further admit to placing 3 tin ash trays on the top of the said piano?"

"I do."

"So that class sing D'ye tinkle plunk John plunk tinkle in his tinkle tinkle zing?"

"They did."

"Were you also a tool of wall street by interfering with the metronome while Musick mistress was singing 'Trees' at the skool concert?"

"I was."

"Did you express the view that even if the Musick mistress was a tree you would not like her planted in your garden?"

"Yes."

"Who invented the first railway engine?"

"Stalin."

"Did you pawn the boxing cup to buy beer?"

"I did."

"Hav Form 3A fallen below output target on Latin sentences?"

"They hav."

"Are you guilty of everything?"

"Very guilty indeed."

The masters are then sent off to their classes looking keen and brisk.

The bell is then rung for big skool and all xemble. Carpets are put down and all smoking forbidden old masters are hung on the walls n.b. rembrandt etc not the deaf master and all is ready. Headmaster sa:

"Do you love the old skool?"

"Yes."

(*it isn't bad sometimes acktually*)

"Do you love the staff?"

"Yes."

"Do you love the skool dog?"

"Yes."

"Wot do you think of the skool food?"

(*A pause*)

"Scrumptous, especially the smoked salmon."

"Will you all sing the skool song."

"Hurra hurra hurra."

"SKOOL-A, *SKOOL*" etc.

After this the boys are manacled to desks and all who die of boredom during french and other lessons are carried out and concealed. Matron is propped up in her chair by wooden stake and skool gardener wakened from deep sleep in onion bed.

The stage is set· *CAVE!* They're coming.

6

HOW TO TORTURE PARENTS

1. *SKOOL PLAYS DISPLAYS BUN FIGHTS AND JAMBOREES*

Once a boy hav been sent to a skool the die is cast. all the same every so often parents wake up and wonder how their little dear is doing. It is then that the headmaster hav to organise a pla or something which prove to parents that their sons are worth their salt and can learn a lot of tricks if pressed like dogs or even seals.

Imagine the scene. i am in 2B just flying a few darts or guided misiles when molesworth 2 sa Hav you heard the latest you are in the skool pla and must wear silk tights chiz chiz chiz. i pause only to tuough him up and zoom off to learn i am to be prince charming curses i shall never live this down.

Acktually not bad as i learn part in big skool after prep and think i am rather super.

La m'dear are you a fairy? Can so pritty a creature be sitting in rags by the fire? I invite you to sup with me etc etc.

As i am saing this amid hale of inkpots darts rags and yells molesworth 2 come up and sa wot are you doing molesworth 1 go on tell me o you might. I am touched by his evident faith and recite the words but he sa if you ask me prince charming is a naughty old man and zoom away. O for peace and solitude to practise my art hem-hem.

When the day of the pla comes all the parents are driven into skool hall and locked in so none can escape. Prince charming zoom upon the stage and pla begin:

PRINCE CHARMING: 'pon my soul it is indeed a pritty wench. Who art thou?

CINDERELLA: I am Cinderella.

PRINCE CHARMING: Thou art not thou art peason with a lot of rouge lipstick and a straw wig and thou lookest like the wrath of god.

CINDERELLA (*dimpling*): And thou molesworth 1 thou canst not call thyself prince charming when thou hast a face like a mad baboon.

PRINCE CHARMING: I will tuough you up for that my pritty maid.

CINDERELLA: Yar boo sucks thou art much too girly in thy white silk tights that are made from i kno not wot. Thou couldst not tuough up a flea ha-ha-hee.

PRINCE CHARMING (*with a low bow*): Wilt thou with me to the ball my sweet one?

CINDERELLA: I hav seen you dancing strip the wilow in our dancing class and i kno you are like 1000 elephants o measly weed. Get thee gone or i will heave the pumpkin at thee.

PRINCE CHARMING: And i will place the fairy mice
down thy unwashed neck.

(*He boweth low and his silk britches bursteth*).

Aktually parents could not stand this kind of strong
meat so we must give them the old soft soap as per
ushual and sa the printed words. They then look
softly at their dear ones and the paters all dream of
the bar at the golf club. One day they will come to see
the pla and get the horid truth.

CINDERELLA ON THE RUN. A PRINCE
CHARMING WHO STUMBLE UPON A
GANGSTERS MOLL. See n. molesworth as a
PRINCE in search of an IDEAL. CERTIFI-
CATE 'X'.

2. *COUNTRY DANCING*

Another form of torture for parents is the displa of
country dancing on ye sham vilage green. The skool
gardener is awakened from another sleep in the onion
bed and skool piano wheeled from big skool revealing
wizard patch of dust marbles dead beetles conkers
and skeletons of boys who hav crept away to die.
Piano is then carted to the green by 99 boys on
ancient wheelbarrow and decorated with laurel leafs
as if that could make the old grid sound any beter.
Boys then all dress up in weedy costumes with all

sorts of bells everywhere and parents take their seats. miss pringle take seat at skool piano and strike huge opning chord.

WAM WAM BONK ZUNK PLUNK
(*dancers enter*)
ALL: Dilly dilly dilly dilly O
With a rilly dilly, strawberry, o.
(*pointing toes*)
Rilly-me Dilly me.
(*jangling a bell on the end of the nose*)
EBENEZER: Rilly-dilly jingle. Rilly-dilly jingle.
EPHRAIM: With a raspberry o.
ALL: Rilly-dilly raspberry rilly-dilly raspberry o.

Piano then goes WAM PLUNK BISH BASH ZUNK while all boys dance like mad bells jangle dogs yap babes cry squadron of heavy bombers fly overhead rane fall molesworth 2 get strangled in the mayploe man call for the telephone bill and gardener canot sleep in the onion bed.

Piano then finish RUNK DUNK RILLY ME REE etc and burst into flames. miss pringle fante and confusion reigns with super charge of mad morris dancers. In fact the only man who can really enjoy all this is the deaf master who sa he hav always liked hiathwatha and look as if he will sing onaway awake beloved for 2 pins.

Of course there are other organised forms of torture for parents recitation of loss of the royal george latin pla duet (n. molesworth and p. peason

Spring song. Mendleson) chorus from mikado cristopher robin carol concerts and not least molesworth 2 who pla mightily his famous piece fairy bells which nothing hav ever been known to stop.

Any case there is only one thing for parents to sa when they recover their speech they must sa it was *much better than last year*. Wot last year must hav been like then is a lot more than i can imagine.

3. *ASSEMBLY OF THE WIZZO SPACE SHIP*

Bung the box containing the model over to your pater and watch his face as he reads the instructions.

HOW TO ASSEMBLE IN 5 MINITS

Your box will contane the folowing parts:

> 1 cormthruster
> 1 envelop
> 6 Wizzo crabbing pins
> 4 Wizzo girders
> 10 special grabs
> 1 computator with vertical helicons

Provide yourself with Wizzo screwdriver and tube of Wizzo concrete paste (from all dealers). Get a metal drill a spirit level and welding set from your toolbox.

Gum the flap (a) to the cormthruster (c) bending

A GAUL returning to Gaul.

towards the Wizzo girders (d) and inserting the crabbing pins. Be careful that the crabbing pins do not touch the special grabs. Iron the envelop (f) and blow it up until it is the size of a foopball and quickly insert Wizzo girders. Pierce the envelop with a Wizzo skewer (from all dealers) and carefully ease the computator into the envelop securing with the grabs. When the computator is in place adjust the helicons by marrying the cormthruster to grabs and crabbing pins.

Your Wizzo Space Ship is now ready for flying.

And your pater after three hours is ready for suicide n.b. as a kindly thort provide a Wizzo sledge hamer for smashing the whole thing to relieve your paters feelings. You will find he sticks to it with the Wizzo concrete paste which is super.

4. READING ALOUD

It hapens very often that parents think they are worred about the progress a boy is making. they do not realise that all boys are numskulls with o branes which is not surprising when you look at the parents really the whole thing goes on and on and there is no stoping it it is a vicious circle.

Some parents try to teach lat arith etc. in the hols but either they don't kno enuff or they loose their tempers and get into a terific bate. Other parents try to give culture etc and this is always disastrous.

PARENT: now nigel we hav a quiet half hour before

bed i will read you the Hapy prince it is a very beatiful story indeed and will bring tears to your eyes.

SKOLAR: O.K. Super smashing and good show.

PARENT: (*in low voice full of emotion*) high above the city on a tall column stood the statue of the Hapy prince nigel will you stop looking out of the window.

SKOLAR: There's a canbera bomber going past. Look zoom wizz ee-auouw.

PARENT: Boys will be boys i supose i will start agane. High above the city on a tall col—

SKOLAR: It's coming back eeeeeeeee-au-ooooooo.

PARENT: (*with patience*) Column stood the statue of the Hapy prince. He was gilded all over with thin leaves of fine gold.

SKOLAR: Machine guns eh-uh-uh-uh-uh-uh-uh.

PARENT: You kno old chap this is an absolutely tip-top tale but it is no use my reading if you are going to shoot down the enemy like that. Please listen.

SKOLAR: I *am* listning.

PARENT: Where was i for eyes he had two bright sapphires and a large—

SKOLAR: How long would it take to fly to the moon?

PARENT: What hav that to do with this beatiful tale of the Hapy prince?

SKOLAR: Absolutely o with some of the planets you would be 823 before you got there.

PARENT: (*sticking to it*) he is as beatiful as a weather-cock remarked one of the town councillors hav you got a handkerchief nigel as this tale gets sad later on a swallow strips the prince of all his gold.

SKOLAR: Did he sell it. O gosh.

PARENT: Why do you sa o gosh. The tale is beatiful becos of the loveliness of the prose it may help you to hav a beter charakter nigel. It may—
(but SKOLAR is not listening he is throing chalk at a black beetle on the window. PARENT chucks the book at him in a collossal rage and stumps off to hav a drink.)

Parent stumps off to hav a drink.

PARENTS AT A GLANCE

I always think character is more
important than brains.

But we *always* give him gin!

I've brought him some chocs, a
comic, an air gun, a pound of
Turkish Delight and can he come
home next Wednesday?

When I was a boy we got
six of the best every day. Made
me what I am.

106

And what's behind this wee door?

No darling Schopenhauer did not *quite* mean that.

I don't care if Mrs Bradbury did run for Britain I'm still going to have a cocktail.

I am sorry about his vest and pants but when he was a little boy he always wore combinations.

I think sometimes parents may wonder whether we
are worth the sacrifices they make for us.

7

SKOOL FOOD

OR THE PIECE OF COD
WHICH PASSETH UNDERSTANDING

1. *ETIQUTTE*

Many boys find themselves quite incapable of making any rude comments on skool food. This is hardly good maners hem-hem and i must impress on all cads and bounders who sa poo gosh when they see a skool sossage to mend their ways.

When faced with a friteful piece of meat which even the skool dog would refuse do not screw up the face in any circs and sa coo ur gosh ghastly. This calls atention to oneself and makes it more difficult to pinch a beter piece from the next boy.

Rice PUDINGS and jely in the poket are not a good mixture with fluff and the ushual nauseating contents. Sometimes you can chiz a bit of pink mange into a hankchief but it is apt to be a bit hard to manage when bloing the nose. peason hav tried green peas up the sleeve but no good really as they all come shooting down again.

We in our skool are proud of our maners which maykth us the weeds we are and when grabber shoot peas from peashooter at the deaf master we are much shoked i do not think. Nor do we make lakes of treacle in the poridge or rivers of gravy through the mashed potatoes perish the thort.

AT TABLE

Acktually whatever boys may sa about skool food the moment deaf master sa lord make us truly etc. whole skool descend upon food with roar like an H bomb and in 2 minits all hav been swept bare. We then hav time for interval of uplifting conversation

i sa e.g.

i think aldous huxley is rather off form in point counterpoint, peason. And he repli i simply couldn't agree with you more rat face but peason is very 4th rate and hav not got beyond buldog drummond. Anyway then the next course come and all boys disappear in a cloud of jely blanch mange plums and aple while treacle tart fly in all directions.

WITHDRAWAL

When the repast is finished the head of the skool or headmaster should wait for a moment until the conversation shows some small signs of flagging then rising to his feet he indicates that the meal is at an end and the lades may withdraw.

Acktually if he waited for the conversation to flag he would be sitting there until tea time when it would all begin agane. Wot he does is to bawl Silence at the top of his voice separate three tuoughs who are

A ROMAN returning to Rome.

III

fiting and the whole skool charge into the coridor except molesworth 2 who is pinching the radio malt.

2. *A NIGHTMARE*

Everbode kno all there is to kno about prunes but anyway the other day i dreamed about them and this is what hapned.

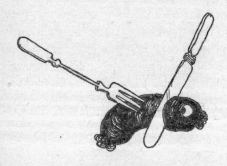

THE REVOLT OF THE PRUNES

by

n. molesworth.

Once upon a time there was a tribe of savvage prunes who lived in a blak mass in the skool pantry.

The prunes had been brought from the prune country where they lived hapily tuoughing each other up and indulging in cotage industries. Then one day JASPER the huge headmaster with huge and hairy hands from grasping the kane descended upon the prunes and caried them off in his case.

So the prunes lay in the pantry and on Mon tue wed thur and fri the cook came in and chose a few to cook for the boys.

At last a prune more savvage then the rest spoke up.

'There is no future in this,' he said. 'Absolutely none at all.'

'And do you hear what they *sa* about us?' said a sensitive prune.

'The only one who eats us is molesworth 2,' piped up another, 'but he would eat anything.'

A fourth said:

'Imagine being inside molesworth 2 with all those comon lozenges spangles carots radio malt and all the other things he hav pinched.'

This thort was so ghastly that the prunes were

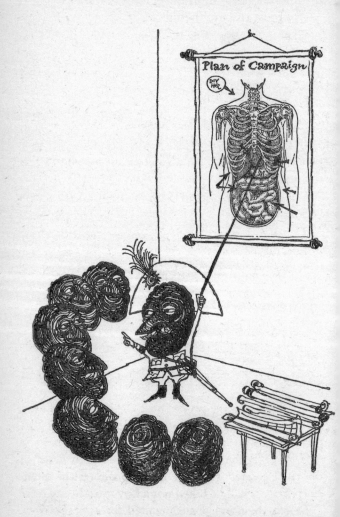

Meanwhile in the prune camp the Revolt had been carefully planned.

silent for 24 hours until the chief prune spoke agane.

'We must rise up,' he sa.

'Exactly,' sa the sensitive prune. 'Why should we revolt them all the time? Why canot they revolt *us*?'

'That's what we'll do,' sa the chief prune. 'We'll have a REVOLT.'

Next day it was the ushual shambles in the skool dining room. Bred pelets flying soup splashing boys yeling when peason sa:

'There are a lot of prunes about toda. i don't like the look of them.'

'*i* don't like the taste of them,' sa molesworth 1 who was a grate wit.

'Can you hear drums?' sa peason. 'what are they drumming for sahib?'

'They are always drumming,' sa molesworth 1. 'Give me a chota peg boy.'

He then call BOY BOY BOY.

No repli.

'They are beating the war drums,' quaver peason. 'My nerves are in shreds.'

'So are your trousis,' sa molesworth wittier than ever.

Meanwhile in the prune camp the Revolt had been carefully planned. The hour would strike when the prunes were to be served.

'JASPER the headmaster must be slain first,' sa the chief prune. 'Then we mop up the rest of them. No prisoners will be taken not a boy must be spared.'

So ten thousand prunes waited for action.

Jasper died horribly.

'Cuh i sa gosh i mean to say its prunes agane,' came the cry from sixty throats.

'Prunes are good for you,' repli the masters in chorus but without conviction.

At that moment the hour struck.

With fierce yells the prunes leapt from plates from dishes from the boxing cup and other hiding places yeling fercely.

JASPER the headmaster was the first victim. When he saw the prunes he gave a yell of fright his false teeth shot across the room and lodged in the opposite wall. The boys noticed no difrence. they thort he was shouting at molesworth 1 as ushual.

While JASPER died horibly all was calm at molesworth's table.

'the trouble with you peason,' sa molesworth 1, 'is that the country is geting you. you need furlo.'

'Its the jungle the ceaseless noise the cries of the jackals.'

'if you can hear a jackal in this dining room you'll be jolly lucky,' sa molesworth.

He larffed a little.

'Perhaps it is we who get on each other's nerves,' sa peason reflectively. Then he jumped up gasping:

'Look the prunes are marching out of the dining room door!'

That was what saved the boys.

The chief prune was a regular soldier and the moment the Revolt broke out he did what all generals do. He burrowed underground and estab-

'Yes sir,' said the G One prune.

lished his headquarters. He had a lot of relations and made them all staff prunes.

Then he poured over the map.

'We should strike here,' said the Chief Prune.

'Yes sir,' said the G One prune.

'Yes sir,' said the G Two prune.

'Yes sir,' said the G Three prune.

But unfortunately he hapned to be pointing at the dining room door so the whole army of prunes marched out of sight and could not be brought into the batle.

It took the skool half an hour to realize that JASPER the headmaster was dead murdered by the prunes. Then all the masters quareled who would wield the kane. At molesworth's table he was recovering from a siesta when the news was brought.

'Dead?' he said. 'By whom?' (Grammer.)

'The prunes are openly revolting.'

molesworth by a grate act of heroism choked back the quip which rose to his lips.

'Sound the alarm,' he cried.

'The alarm went off at ten to four.'

'Then to horse.'

'There is only one horse,' replied peason paying him back in his own coin.' They are on the playing fields.'

'This,' said molesworth, 'is one batle which will be won on the playing fields of eat 'em.'

But there was no responsive larffter.

'This,' sa molesworth 1, 'is one batle which will be won – oh well carry on.'

The prunes encamped on the onion bed the boys on the criket pitch.

All through the night the oposing forces watched each other. Down in the headquarters both staffs pored over their maps and there was fitful conversation. The boys were very serious. they realized what would hapen if the prunes won. They would be put in the larder and the prunes would complane about them.

'Boys agane toda ugh,' the prunes would sa.

And what they would sa when they tasted molesworth 2 canot be imagined.

'Let us strike here,' said the duke of molesworth. 'Form square men.'

'A square man?' said peason. 'Who ever heard of that?'

'Only the general can make jokes,' molesworth said coldly.

'To horse!' cried peason.

'One horse will do,' said the duke, larffing.

Honour was satisfied.

'CHARGE!' he ordered.

And so the two armies moved against each other but owing to headquarters they missed. One army fell in the river, the other in the duck pond.

The noise in fact was so grate that it woke JASPER the headmaster who had not been murdered at all but was thinking of latin sentences. With a croak of rage he grasped his kane and rolled out cursing in the name of Beelzebub. He gave six of the best to every boy on sight but i am glad to sa that the prunes were all drowned in the duck pond.

It was a sad loss to JASPER but there was only one thing to do. He sat down and ordered some more.

All drowned in the duck pond.

CURTAIN SPEECH

Well that is all there is to kno about skool but it is
alright becos the end of the term is in sight cheers
cheers cheers. All boys get together with super rags
wheezes japes and pranks. Down with the masters no
more latin no more french no more sitting on the hard
old bench no more earwigs in our stew etc. Pilow
fights and feasts in the dorm. Noble boys make
bonfires of skool books and toast the staff slowly in
the flames Charge at everbode and zoom around.

So the bus arives goodbye to all goodbye to skool
pig and skool dog to matron one and all sa hav a
good hols we weep with joy. Goodbye headmaster
goodbye peason acktually you are joly d. and it is sad
to leave. Goodbye to all goodbye.

The Armada Lion Book of Humorous Verse

CHOSEN BY RUTH PETRIE

Here's humorous verse from Edward Lear, Lewis Carroll, Hilaire Belloc, G. K. Chesterton, Kenneth Grahame, John Betjeman, Ted Hughes, Spike Milligan, Michael Flanders, Roy Fuller and many more.

Poets well-known and unknown offer humour and nonsense of every sort.

There's even '. . . a young man of Japan
Whose limericks never would scan;
  When they said it was so,
  He replied, "Yes I know,
But I always try to get as many
words into the last line as ever I possibly can".'

Whispering in the Wind

ALAN MARSHALL

Once upon a time . . . there was a bunyip who kept guard over the last Beautiful Princess in Australia. Now she was just what a beautiful princess *should* be, but the Bunyip was hardly a typical guard – wombat, kangaroo, giraffe and dragon all rolled into one, then covered with fur! And he squirted people to death, for as he said, 'It's clean and wholesome and doesn't leave a mess.'

Peter and his kangaroo companion, Greyfur, had journeyed a long way to rescue the Beautiful Princess. They'd fought off the Giant and the Pale Witch, and outsmarted the Doubt Cats. But how were they to defeat an enemy like the Bunyip who invited them to lunch – fried frogs – and then said he'd give them a fifty yards' start before squirting them to kingdom come . . .?

The Sword in the Stone

T. H. WHITE

Probably only the magician, Merlyn, knew that his pupil, the Wart (to rhyme with 'Art') would one day be the great King Arthur.

For six years Merlyn was the boy's tutor and the Wart learned all manner of useful things; such as what it is like to be a fish or a hawk or a badger.

Then the king, Pendragon, died without heirs. And King Pellinore arrived at the court with an extraordinary story of a sword stuck in an anvil stuck to a stone outside a church in London. Written on the sword in gold letters were the words

Whoso Pulleth Out This Sword of
This Stone and Anvil, is Rightwise
King Born of All England.

The last person anybody expected to pull out the sword was the Wart but then he had had Merlyn as his tutor for the past six years.

The Donkey Rustlers

GERALD DURRELL

This lively story with a Greek island setting tells how Amanda and David plot to outwit the unpleasant local mayor and help their Greek friend, Yani. The villagers, and especially the mayor, depend on their donkeys for transport. If the children are to blackmail them successfully the donkeys must disappear – and disappear they do, to the consternation of the whole village . . .

Told in Gerald Durrell's dashing style with his own particular brand of humour, this story will be eagerly read by older children.

The Outsiders

S. E. HINTON

'You know what a greaser is?' Bob asked. 'White trash with long hair.'

I felt the blood draining from my face. 'You know what a Soc is? White trash with Mustangs and madras.' And then, because I couldn't think of anything bad enough to call them, I spat at them.

Bob shook his head, smiling slowly. 'You could use a bath, greaser. And a good working over.'

The Soc caught my arm and twisted it behind my back, and shoved my face into the fountain. I fought, but the hand at the back of my neck was strong. I'm drowning, I thought, they've gone too far . . .

The Outsiders is an authentic and moving book written by a teenager about teenagers. It was published originally in America where it has already sold over 750,000 copies in paperback.

The Greatest Gresham

GILLIAN AVERY

The three Greshams were prim, correct Victorian children, ruled by 'what other people might think' —but in their hearts they longed to be something quite different. The two Holts *were* quite different, and in the Greshams' eyes totally 'unsuitable'. They read at the table, ate sweets between meals and swung on their front gate!

But Richard decided to take the Greshams in hand, for he felt they ought to develop 'an independent mind'. And so 'The Society for the Achieving of Greatness, Broadening of Horizons, Enlarging of Ideas, and the Cultivating of Independent Minds' was born.

The rules were uncompromising—Amy had to renounce her precious pink rabbit, Julia to travel to Westminster Abbey in a railway carriage (but the Greshams were forbidden to venture from their front door alone!), and poor Henry to climb the apple tree. All this in the name of 'Greatness'!